# Adding and taking away

$3 + \boxed{8}$

$6 + \boxed{\phantom{0}}$

$\boxed{\phantom{0}} + 7$ $\quad 11$

$9 + \boxed{\phantom{0}}$

$2 + \boxed{\phantom{0}}$

$8 + \boxed{\phantom{0}}$

$\boxed{\phantom{0}} + 9$ $\quad 12$

$6 + \boxed{\phantom{0}}$

$\boxed{\phantom{0}} + 9$

$\boxed{\phantom{0}} + 11$ $\quad 13$

$5 + \boxed{\phantom{0}}$

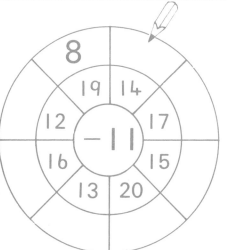

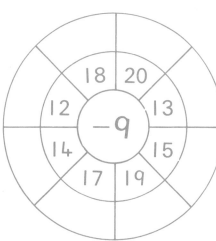

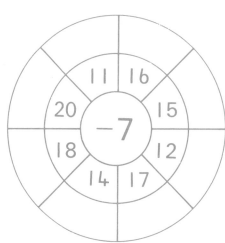

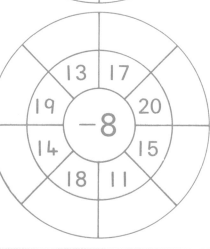

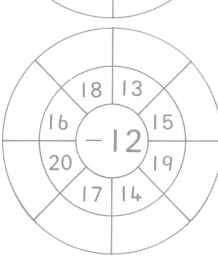

$9 + \boxed{\phantom{0}}$

$8 + \boxed{\phantom{0}}$

$14 + \boxed{\phantom{0}}$ $\quad 18$

$\boxed{\phantom{0}} + 6$

$11 + \boxed{\phantom{0}}$

$6 + \boxed{\phantom{0}}$

$\boxed{\phantom{0}} + 10$ $\quad 19$

$4 + \boxed{\phantom{0}}$

$15 + \boxed{\phantom{0}}$

$3 + \boxed{\phantom{0}}$

$\boxed{\phantom{0}} + 7$ $\quad 20$

$9 + \boxed{\phantom{0}}$

# Counting in 2s

19  18  20  3

16  1  4

15  14  17  2  6

13

5

11  9  8

12  10  7

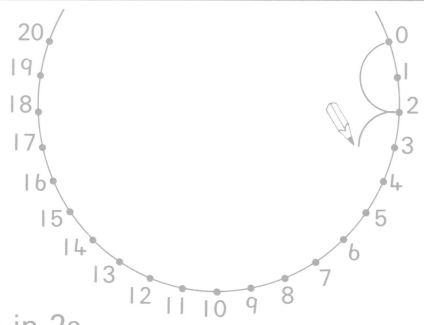

## Count on in 2s

0 ⟶ 2        10 ⟶ ☐        4 ⟶ ☐

6 ⟶ ☐        8 ⟶ ☐         12 ⟶ ☐

2 ⟶ ☐        14 ⟶ ☐        18 ⟶ ☐

3 × 2 = 6        1 × 2 = ☐        4 × 2 = ☐

8 × 2 = ☐        10 × 2 = ☐       7 × 2 = ☐

5 × 2 = ☐        6 × 2 = ☐        9 × 2 = ☐

# Picture problems

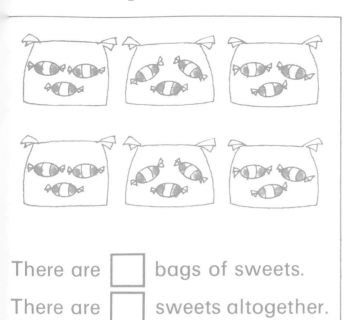

There are ☐ bags of sweets.

There are ☐ sweets altogether.

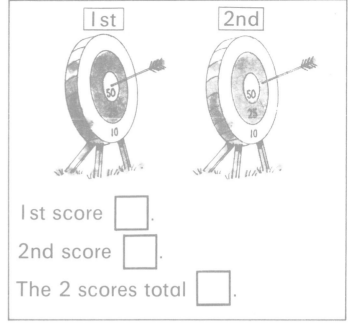

1st score ☐ .

2nd score ☐ .

The 2 scores total ☐ .

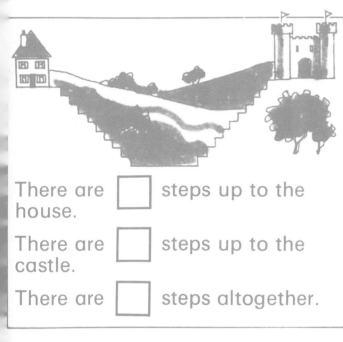

There are ☐ steps up to the house.

There are ☐ steps up to the castle.

There are ☐ steps altogether.

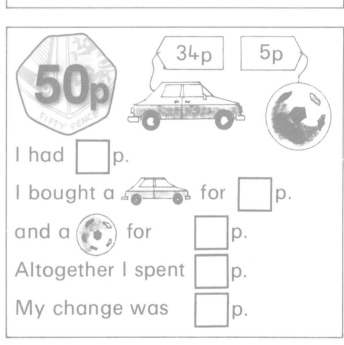

I had ☐ p.

I bought a 🚗 for ☐ p.

and a ⚽ for ☐ p.

Altogether I spent ☐ p.

My change was ☐ p.

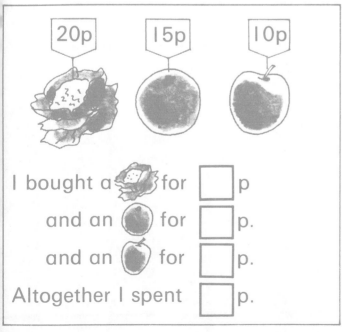

I bought a 🥗 for ☐ p

and an 🍊 for ☐ p.

and an 🍎 for ☐ p.

Altogether I spent ☐ p.

There are ☐ bananas.

The monkeys have ☐ bananas each.

# Schofield & Sims

the long-established educational publisher
specialising in maths, English and science materials for schools

**Number Book** is a series of graded activity books helping children to learn basic calculation skills, including addition, subtraction, multiplication and division.

**Number Book 4** includes:

• Multiplication and division by 2 and 3
• Tens and units; counting in tens
• Number facts (for example, pairs of numbers that add up to 20)
• Using a hundred square
• Recognising coins to 50p, counting money and giving change
• Vertical addition and subtraction (without borrowing or carrying).

This book is suitable for children making the transition from Key Stage 1 to Key Stage 2.

**The full range of titles in the series is as follows:**

**Number Book 1:**      ISBN 978 07217 0788 4

**Number Book 2:**      ISBN 978 07217 0789 1

**Number Book 3:**      ISBN 978 07217 0790 7

**Number Book 4:**      ISBN 978 07217 0791 4

**Number Book 5:**      ISBN 978 07217 0792 1

Have you tried **Problem Solving** by Schofield & Sims?
This series helps children to sharpen their mathematical skills by applying their knowledge to a range of number problems and 'real-life' contexts.

**For further information and to place your order
visit www.schofieldandsims.co.uk or telephone 01484 607080**

ISBN 978 07217 0791 4

£2.45
(Retail price)

**Key Stage 1**
**Age range: 5–7 years**
(Books at either end of the series incorporate some overlap with earlier and later key stages to support transition)

ISBN 978-07217-0791-4

9 780721 707914

Schofield & Sims

Dogley Mill, Fenay Bridge, Huddersfield HD8 0NQ
Phone: 01484 607080 Facsimile: 01484 606815
E-mail: sales@schofieldandsims.co.uk

# Schofield & Sims

# Number Book 4

Name

# Number Book 4

The Number Books are a series of five workbooks
by Andrew Parker and Jane Stamford.

Number Book 1    978 07217 0788 4
Number Book 2    978 07217 0789 1
Number Book 3    978 07217 0790 7
Number Book 4    978 07217 0791 4
Number Book 5    978 07217 0792 1

## Notes for the Teacher

This book continues the practice in computation with numbers
up to 100. The work is graded and gives plenty of examples and
practice in vertical addition and subtraction with some carrying
figures, mapping, number wheels, and a number square.
The book covers:

Addition of numbers up to 100
Subtraction of numbers below 100
2s, (2) and ÷ 2
3s, (3) and ÷ 3
Counting on
10s
10s and 1s
Addition of 10s and 1s
Subtraction of 10s and 1s
Recognition of coins and drawing values,
using coins up to 50p
Shopping – adding two items up to 50p
– change from amounts up to 50p
Picture problems

The instructions are kept to a minimum as the work is
self-explanatory.

978 07217 0791 4

First printed © 1982
This edition © 1990
Twenty ninth impression 2013

## Schofield&Sims

Printed in England by Wyndeham Gait Ltd., Grimsby.
Cover design & illustration by Curve Creative, Bradford.

# Sharing between 2

Share  $\boxed{1}$ each

$$2 \div 2 = \boxed{1}$$

Share 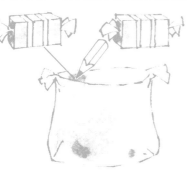 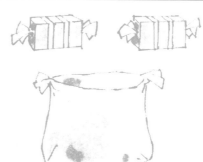 $\boxed{\phantom{0}}$ each

$$4 \div 2 = \boxed{\phantom{0}}$$

Share 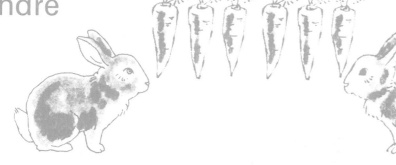 $\boxed{\phantom{0}}$ each

$$6 \div 2 = \boxed{\phantom{0}}$$

Share  $\boxed{\phantom{0}}$ each

$$8 \div 2 = \boxed{\phantom{0}}$$

Share  $\boxed{\phantom{0}}$ each

$$10 \div 2 = \boxed{\phantom{0}}$$

# Sharing between 2

Share

☐ each

$12 \div 2 =$ ☐

Share

☐ each

$14 \div 2 =$ ☐

Share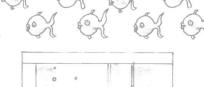

☐ each

$16 \div 2 =$ ☐

Share

☐ each

$18 \div 2 =$ ☐

Share

☐ each

$20 \div 2 =$ ☐

## 2s

2 ÷ 2 = ☐ 1     4 ÷ 2 = ☐     6 ÷ 2 = ☐

8 ÷ 2 = ☐     10 ÷ 2 = ☐     12 ÷ 2 = ☐

14 ÷ 2 = ☐     16 ÷ 2 = ☐     18 ÷ 2 = ☐

            20 ÷ 2 = ☐

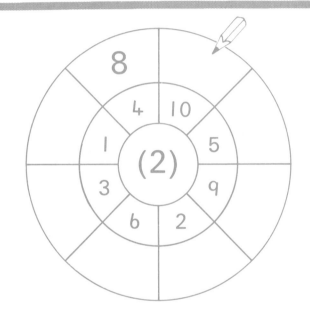 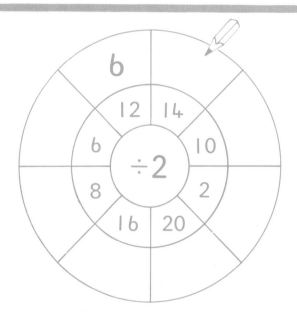

2 × 2 = ☐     4 ÷ 2 = ☐     10 × 2 = ☐

16 ÷ 2 = ☐     20 ÷ 2 = ☐     6 × 2 = ☐

8 ÷ 2 = ☐     1 × 2 = ☐     12 ÷ 2 = ☐

4 × 2 = ☐     2 ÷ 2 = ☐     18 ÷ 2 = ☐

10 ÷ 2 = ☐     3 × 2 = ☐     9 × 2 = ☐

8 × 2 = ☐     14 ÷ 2 = ☐     5 × 2 = ☐

6 ÷ 2 = ☐                        7 × 2 = ☐

# Counting in 10s

= $\boxed{10}$

= ☐

= ☐

= ☐

= ☐

= ☐

= ☐

= ☐

= ☐

= ☐

8

# 10s and 1s

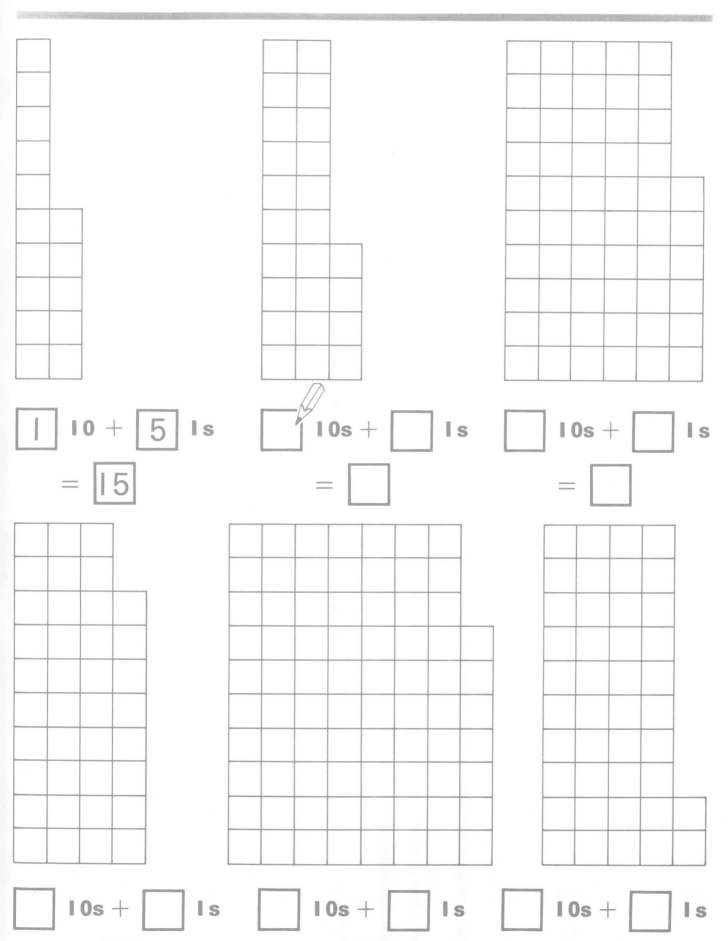

| | 10 + | 5 | 1s | | 10s + | | 1s | | 10s + | | 1s |

= | 15 |          = | |          = | |

| | 10s + | | 1s          | | 10s + | | 1s          | | 10s + | | 1s

= | |          = | |          = | |

# 10s and 1s

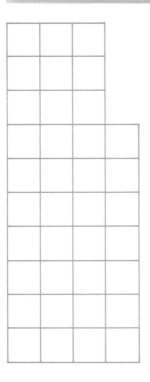
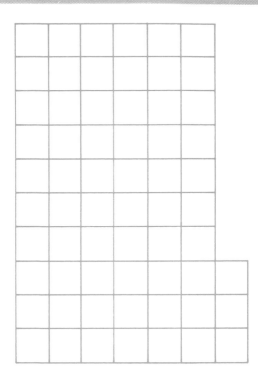
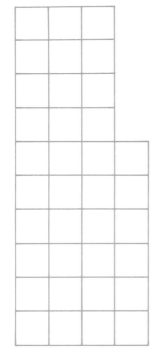

| ⬚ 10s + ⬚ 1s | ⬚ 10s + ⬚ 1s | ⬚ 10s + ⬚ 1s |
| = ⬚ | = ⬚ | = ⬚ |

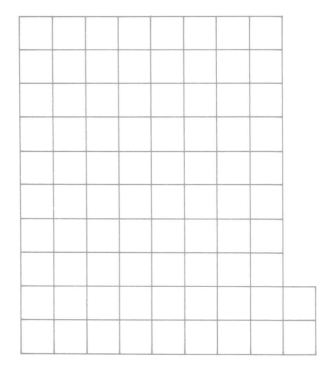
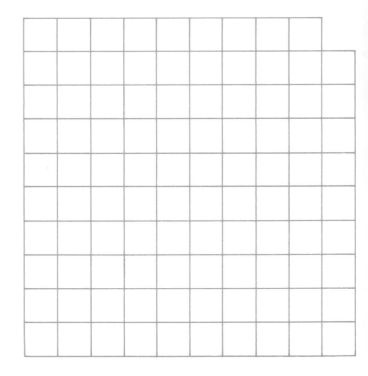

⬚ 10s + ⬚ 1s          ⬚ 10s + ⬚ 1s

= ⬚                    = ⬚

# 10s and 1s

2 10s and 4 1s = $\boxed{24}$

2 10s and 8 1s = ☐

8 10s and 3 1s = ☐

3 10s and 6 1s = ☐

4 10s and 8 1s = ☐

4 10s and 2 1s = ☐

5 10s and 7 1s = ☐

6 10s and 9 1s = ☐

7 10s and 3 1s = ☐

9 10s and 5 1s = ☐

6 10s and 0 1s = ☐

7 10s and 2 1s = ☐

8 10s and 8 1s = ☐

5 10s and 5 1s = ☐

9 10s and 9 1s = ☐

8 10s and 9 1s = ☐

19 = $\boxed{1}$ 10 and $\boxed{9}$ 1s

34 = ☐ 10s and ☐ 1s

53 = ☐ 10s and ☐ 1s

78 = ☐ 10s and ☐ 1s

20 = ☐ 10s and ☐ 1s

65 = ☐ 10s and ☐ 1s

47 = ☐ 10s and ☐ 1s

59 = ☐ 10s and ☐ 1s

46 = ☐ 10s and ☐ 1s

92 = ☐ 10s and ☐ 1s

37 = ☐ 10s and ☐ 1s

25 = ☐ 10s and ☐ 1s

12 = ☐ 10 and ☐ 1s

84 = ☐ 10s and ☐ 1s

71 = ☐ 10s and ☐ 1

100 = ☐ 10s and ☐ 1s

# Using a 100 square

| 1 | 2 | 3 | 4 | 5 | 6 | 7 | 8 | 9 | 10 |
|---|---|---|---|---|---|---|---|---|---|
| 11 | 12 | 13 | 14 | 15 | 16 | 17 | 18 | 19 | 20 |
| 21 | 22 | 23 | 24 | 25 | 26 | 27 | 28 | 29 | 30 |
| 31 | 32 | 33 | 34 | 35 | 36 | 37 | 38 | 39 | 40 |
| 41 | 42 | 43 | 44 | 45 | 46 | 47 | 48 | 49 | 50 |
| 51 | 52 | 53 | 54 | 55 | 56 | 57 | 58 | 59 | 60 |
| 61 | 62 | 63 | 64 | 65 | 66 | 67 | 68 | 69 | 70 |
| 71 | 72 | 73 | 74 | 75 | 76 | 77 | 78 | 79 | 80 |
| 81 | 82 | 83 | 84 | 85 | 86 | 87 | 88 | 89 | 90 |
| 91 | 92 | 93 | 94 | 95 | 96 | 97 | 98 | 99 | 100 |

## Count on 10 and colour

5 → 15    21 → ☐    52 → ☐    33 → ☐    41 → ☐

7 → ☐    37 → ☐    71 → ☐    81 → ☐    90 → ☐

13 → ☐    45 → ☐    26 → ☐    38 → ☐    42 → ☐

19 → ☐    46 → ☐    74 → ☐    83 → ☐    75 → ☐

34 → ☐    38 → ☐    64 → ☐    56 → ☐    67 → ☐

# Adding 10

$1 + 10 = \square$ $\qquad$ $15 + 10 = \square$ $\qquad$ $18 + 10 = \square$ $\qquad$ $20 + 10 = \square$

$27 + 10 = \square$ $\qquad$ $37 + 10 = \square$ $\qquad$ $41 + 10 = \square$ $\qquad$ $48 + 10 = \square$

$52 + 10 = \square$ $\qquad$ $58 + 10 = \square$ $\qquad$ $63 + 10 = \square$ $\qquad$ $67 + 10 = \square$

$74 + 10 = \square$ $\qquad$ $77 + 10 = \square$ $\qquad$ $86 + 10 = \square$ $\qquad$ $90 + 10 = \square$

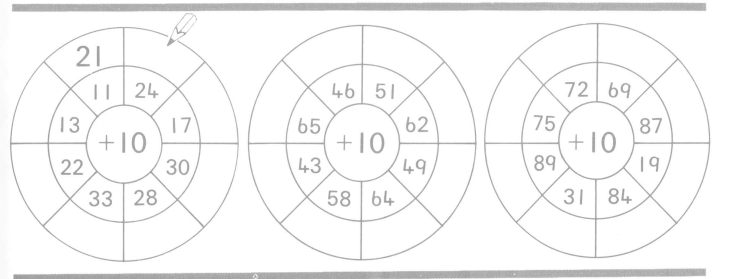

$4 + 10 = \square$ $\qquad$ $9 + 10 = \square$ $\qquad$ $82 + 10 = \square$ $\qquad$ $23 + 10 = \square$

$16 + 10 = \square$ $\qquad$ $38 + 10 = \square$ $\qquad$ $66 + 10 = \square$ $\qquad$ $54 + 10 = \square$

$32 + 10 = \square$ $\qquad$ $76 + 10 = \square$ $\qquad$ $29 + 10 = \square$ $\qquad$ $40 + 10 = \square$

$57 + 10 = \square$ $\qquad$ $21 + 10 = \square$ $\qquad$ $78 + 10 = \square$ $\qquad$ $88 + 10 = \square$

$12$ $\xrightarrow{+10}$ $\bigcirc$ $\xrightarrow{+10}$ $\bigcirc$ $\xrightarrow{+10}$ $\bigcirc$ $\xrightarrow{+10}$ $\bigcirc$

$59$ $\xrightarrow{+10}$ $\bigcirc$ $\xrightarrow{+10}$ $\bigcirc$ $\xrightarrow{+10}$ $\bigcirc$ $\xrightarrow{+10}$ $\bigcirc$

# Taking away 10

11 − 10 = ☐    17 − 10 = ☐    19 − 10 = ☐    24 − 10 = ☐

26 − 10 = ☐    31 − 10 = ☐    38 − 10 = ☐    42 − 10 = ☐

45 − 10 = ☐    53 − 10 = ☐    67 − 10 = ☐    74 − 10 = ☐

82 − 10 = ☐    95 − 10 = ☐    98 − 10 = ☐    100 − 10 = ☐

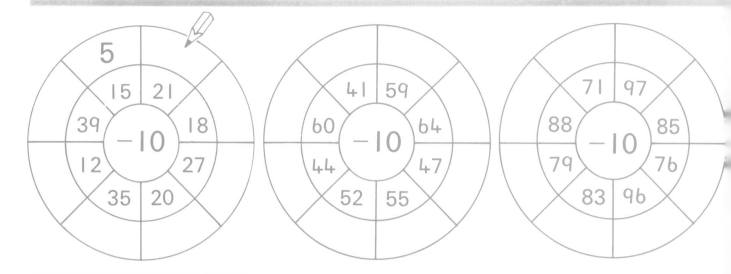

29 − 10 = ☐    62 − 10 = ☐    36 − 10 = ☐    87 − 10 = ☐

70 − 10 = ☐    13 − 10 = ☐    69 − 10 = ☐    48 − 10 = ☐

91 − 10 = ☐    49 − 10 = ☐    22 − 10 = ☐    93 − 10 = ☐

58 − 10 = ☐    33 − 10 = ☐    80 − 10 = ☐    99 − 10 = ☐

44 →(−10)→ ◯ →(−10)→ ◯ →(−10)→ ◯ →(−10)→ ◯

99 →(−10)→ ◯ →(−10)→ ◯ →(−10)→ ◯ →(−10)→ ◯

# Adding and taking away 10

14 + 10 = ☐    25 + 10 = ☐    47 + 10 = ☐    71 + 10 = ☐

61 + 10 = ☐    50 + 10 = ☐    34 + 10 = ☐    85 + 10 = ☐

16 − 10 = ☐    28 − 10 = ☐    77 − 10 = ☐    40 − 10 = ☐

94 − 10 = ☐    32 − 10 = ☐    43 − 10 = ☐    57 − 10 = ☐

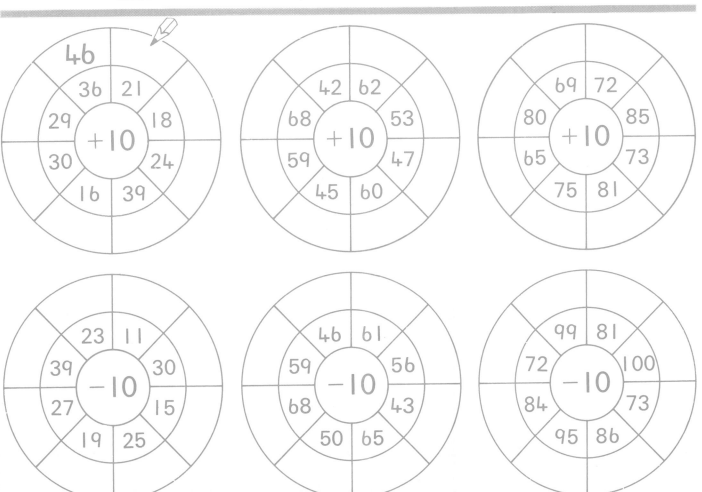

12 + 10 = ☐    35 + 10 = ☐    54 − 10 = ☐    73 + 10 = ☐

46 − 10 = ☐    55 + 10 = ☐    66 − 10 = ☐    34 − 10 = ☐

26 + 10 = ☐    75 − 10 = ☐    79 + 10 = ☐    44 + 10 = ☐

78 − 10 = ☐    83 + 10 = ☐    14 − 10 = ☐    92 − 10 = ☐

# Adding 10s and 1s

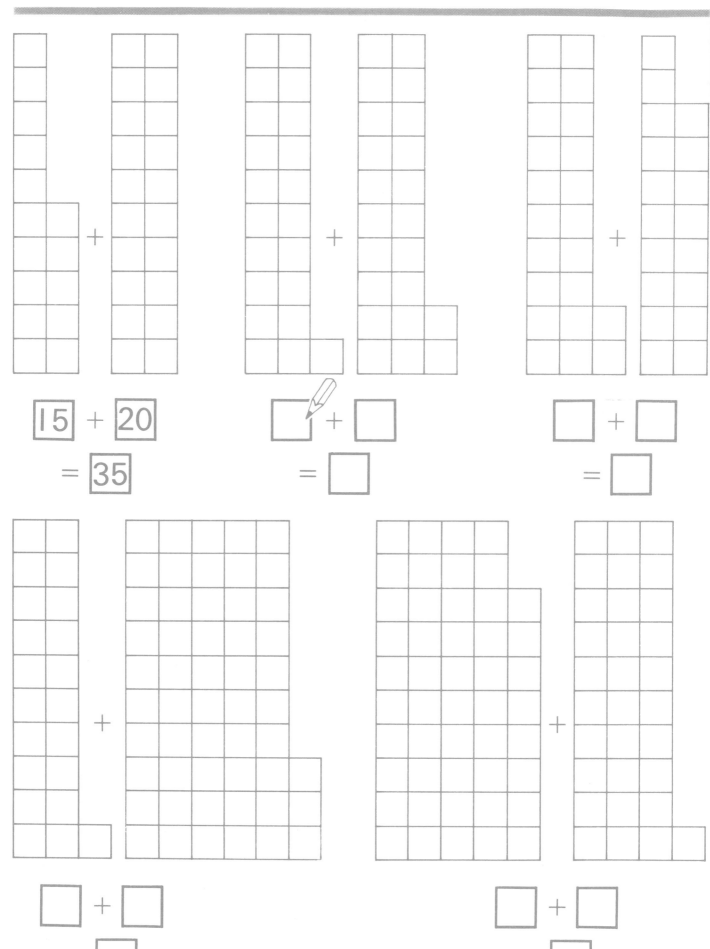

$\boxed{15} + \boxed{20}$

$= \boxed{35}$

$\boxed{\phantom{0}} + \boxed{\phantom{0}}$

$= \boxed{\phantom{0}}$

$\boxed{\phantom{0}} + \boxed{\phantom{0}}$

$= \boxed{\phantom{0}}$

$\boxed{\phantom{0}} + \boxed{\phantom{0}}$

$= \boxed{\phantom{0}}$

$\boxed{\phantom{0}} + \boxed{\phantom{0}}$

$= \boxed{\phantom{0}}$

# Adding

15 + 2 = ☐    21 + 4 = ☐    25 + 3 = ☐    27 + 2 = ☐

31 + 5 = ☐    36 + 2 = ☐    38 + 1 = ☐    41 + 8 = ☐

45 + 3 = ☐    47 + 1 = ☐    52 + 7 = ☐    65 + 4 = ☐

72 + 5 = ☐    81 + 6 = ☐    84 + 4 = ☐    92 + 7 = ☐

---

```
  16        14        15        21        32        33
+  2      +  3      +  4      +  7      +  6      +  5
----      ----      ----      ----      ----      ----
  18
```

```
  44        53        62        74         5         6
+  5      +  3      +  7      +  2      + 81      + 93
----      ----      ----      ----      ----      ----
```

```
  20        34        14        46        55        27
+ 11      + 21      + 23      + 32      + 24      + 31
----      ----      ----      ----      ----      ----
```

---

```
  13        13        27        24        21        35
+ 12      + 16      + 11      + 15      + 36      + 22
----      ----      ----      ----      ----      ----
```

```
  42        41        32        57        15        63
+ 31      + 35      + 54      + 21      + 62      + 26
----      ----      ----      ----      ----      ----
```

```
  11        75        71        81        84        86
+ 78      + 24      + 26      + 12      + 14      + 13
----      ----      ----      ----      ----      ----
```

# Taking away

$16 - 3 = \boxed{\phantom{00}}$   $18 - 6 = \boxed{\phantom{00}}$   $22 - 1 = \boxed{\phantom{00}}$   $28 - 4 = \boxed{\phantom{00}}$

$32 - 2 = \boxed{\phantom{00}}$   $37 - 3 = \boxed{\phantom{00}}$   $39 - 8 = \boxed{\phantom{00}}$   $45 - 1 = \boxed{\phantom{00}}$

$47 - 7 = \boxed{\phantom{00}}$   $49 - 9 = \boxed{\phantom{00}}$   $55 - 5 = \boxed{\phantom{00}}$   $64 - 3 = \boxed{\phantom{00}}$

$76 - 5 = \boxed{\phantom{00}}$   $84 - 3 = \boxed{\phantom{00}}$   $89 - 8 = \boxed{\phantom{00}}$   $95 - 1 = \boxed{\phantom{00}}$

| 18 | 15 | 19 | 25 | 38 | 39 |
|---|---|---|---|---|---|
| − 6 | − 4 | − 8 | − 3 | − 6 | − 7 |

| 48 | 27 | 36 | 38 | 46 | 48 |
|---|---|---|---|---|---|
| − 5 | − 11 | − 14 | − 21 | − 23 | − 37 |

| 55 | 58 | 65 | 73 | 84 | 99 |
|---|---|---|---|---|---|
| − 44 | − 32 | − 14 | − 31 | − 42 | − 89 |

| 15 | 18 | 23 | 28 | 36 | 39 |
|---|---|---|---|---|---|
| − 11 | − 11 | − 12 | − 14 | − 16 | − 17 |

| 45 | 47 | 53 | 56 | 63 | 69 |
|---|---|---|---|---|---|
| − 25 | − 24 | − 31 | − 43 | − 41 | − 57 |

| 74 | 79 | 82 | 87 | 95 | 99 |
|---|---|---|---|---|---|
| − 32 | − 61 | − 31 | − 52 | − 74 | − 66 |

# Adding and taking away

15 + 5 = ☐  11 + 13 = ☐  21 + 18 = ☐  32 + 21 = ☐

32 − 11 = ☐  46 − 23 = ☐  58 − 21 = ☐  67 − 32 = ☐

24 + 22 = ☐  54 − 33 = ☐  21 + 35 = ☐  39 − 18 = ☐

44 + 33 = ☐  25 + 61 = ☐  96 − 82 = ☐  79 − 63 = ☐

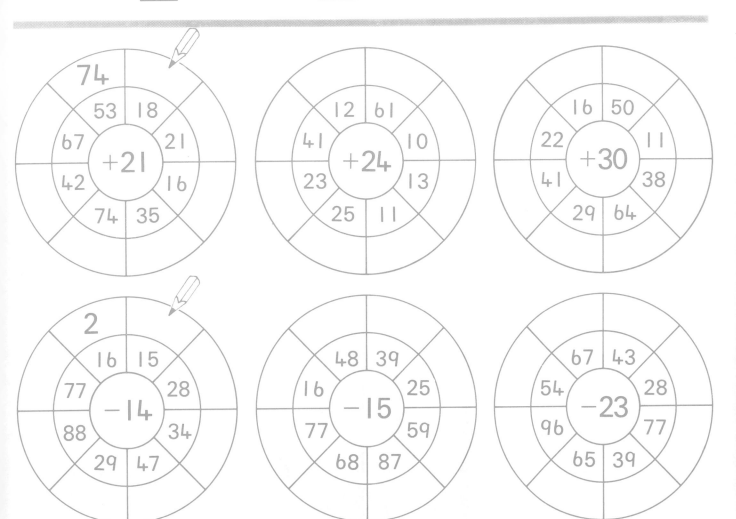

|  |  |  |  |  |  |
|---|---|---|---|---|---|
| 28 <br> + 41 | 33 <br> + 54 | 87 <br> − 25 | 58 <br> + 41 | 85 <br> − 52 | 36 <br> − 14 |
| 97 <br> − 32 | 54 <br> + 44 | 33 <br> − 11 | 75 <br> − 43 | 81 <br> + 18 | 69 <br> − 36 |

# How much money ?

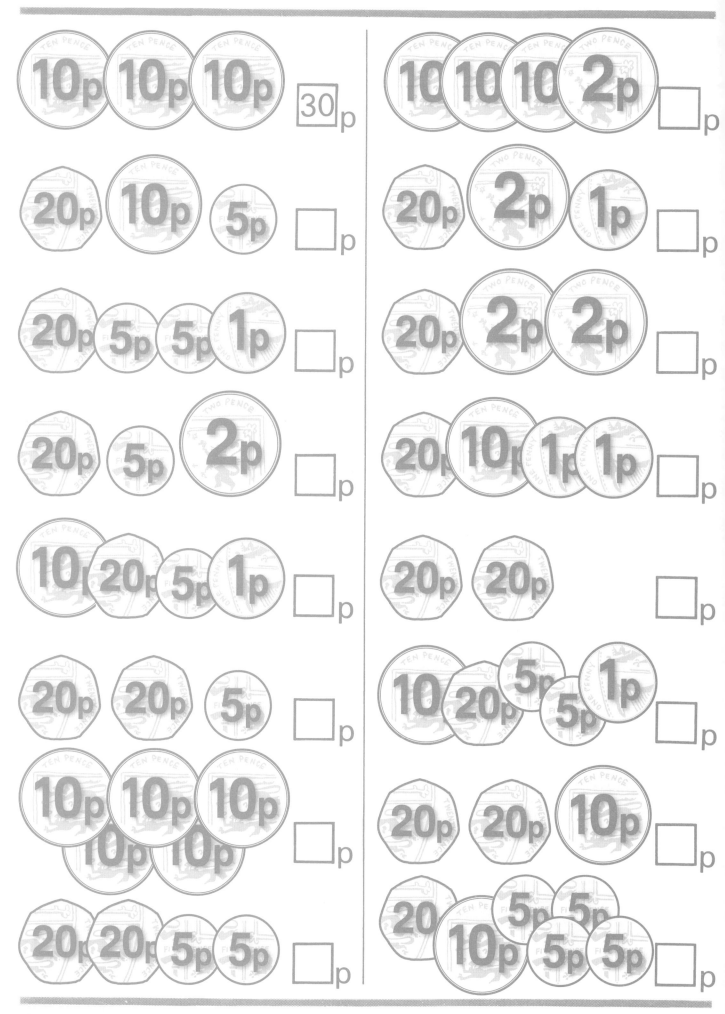

| Coins | Answer |
|---|---|
| 10p 10p 10p | 30p |
| 20p 10p 5p | ☐p |
| 20p 5p 5p 1p | ☐p |
| 20p 5p 2p | ☐p |
| 10p 20p 5p 1p | ☐p |
| 20p 20p 5p | ☐p |
| 10p 10p 10p 10p 10p | ☐p |
| 20p 20p 5p 5p | ☐p |
| 10p 10p 10p 2p | ☐p |
| 20p 2p 1p | ☐p |
| 20p 2p 2p | ☐p |
| 20p 10p 1p 1p | ☐p |
| 20p 20p | ☐p |
| 10p 20p 5p 5p 1p | ☐p |
| 20p 20p 10p | ☐p |
| 20p 10p 5p 5p 5p | ☐p |

20

# Draw the money in the purses

Use **20p** with **10p** **5p** **2p** and **1p** coins

25p

27p

28p

31p

36p

39p

42p

48p

50p

21

# Shopping

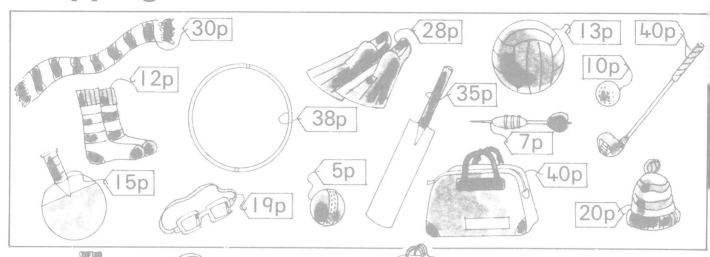

 □p + □p = □p      □p + □p = □p

□p + □p = □p      □p + □p = □p

□p + □p = □p      □p + □p = □p

□p + □p = □p      □p + □p = □p

30p – □p = □p      35p – □p = □p

40p – □p = □p      40p – □p = □p

45p – □p = □p      48p – □p = □p

50p – □p = □p      50p – □p = □p

# How many coins make 50p?

50p

| Use **2p** | Use **5p** | Use **10p** | Use **20p** and **10p** |
|---|---|---|---|
| 2p | | | |

# 3s

| | | |
|---|---|---|
| Give the hand 3 rings | ☐ | rings |
| Give each coat 3 buttons | ☐ | buttons |
| Give each hat 3 cherries | ☐ | cherries |
| Give each glass 3 straws | ☐ | straws |
| Give each tree 3 leaves | ☐ | leaves |
| Give each purse 3 pennies | ☐ | pennies |
| Give each castle 3 flags | ☐ | flags |
| Give each ladybird 3 spots | ☐ | spots |
| Give each bag 3 sweets | ☐ | sweets |
| Give each cake 3 candles | ☐ | candles |

24

# Count the legs on the stools

1 stool has ☐ legs.

2 stools have ☐ + ☐ = ☐ legs.

3 stools have ☐ + ☐ + ☐ = ☐ legs.

4 stools have ☐ + ☐ + ☐ + ☐ = ☐ legs.

5 stools have ☐ + ☐ + ☐ + ☐ + ☐ = ☐ legs.

6 stools have ☐ + ☐ + ☐ + ☐ + ☐ + ☐ = ☐ legs.

7 stools have ☐ + ☐ + ☐ + ☐ + ☐ + ☐ + ☐ = ☐ legs.

8 stools have ☐ + ☐ + ☐ + ☐ + ☐ + ☐ + ☐ + ☐ = ☐ legs.

9 stools have ☐ + ☐ + ☐ + ☐ + ☐ + ☐ + ☐ + ☐ + ☐ = ☐ legs.

10 stools have ☐ + ☐ + ☐ + ☐ + ☐ + ☐ + ☐ + ☐ + ☐ + ☐ = ☐ legs.

| Number of stools | 1 | 2 | 3 | 4 | 5 | 6 | 7 | 8 | 9 | 10 |
|---|---|---|---|---|---|---|---|---|---|---|
| Number of legs | | | | | | | | | | |

25

# Colour the 3 family

| 1 | 2 | 3 | 4 | 5 | 6 | 7 | 8 | 9 | 10 |
|---|---|---|---|---|---|---|---|---|---|
| 11 | 12 | 13 | 14 | 15 | 16 | 17 | 18 | 19 | 20 |
| 21 | 22 | 23 | 24 | 25 | 26 | 27 | 28 | 29 | 30 |

## Write the 3 family

| 3 | 6 | | | | | | | | |
|---|---|---|---|---|---|---|---|---|---|

$1 \times 3 = \boxed{\phantom{0}}$   $2 \times 3 = \boxed{\phantom{0}}$   $3 \times 3 = \boxed{\phantom{0}}$

$4 \times 3 = \boxed{\phantom{0}}$   $5 \times 3 = \boxed{\phantom{0}}$   $6 \times 3 = \boxed{\phantom{0}}$

$7 \times 3 = \boxed{\phantom{0}}$   $8 \times 3 = \boxed{\phantom{0}}$   $9 \times 3 = \boxed{\phantom{0}}$

$10 \times 3 = \boxed{\phantom{0}}$

$5 \times 3 = \boxed{\phantom{0}}$   $9 \times 3 = \boxed{\phantom{0}}$   $1 \times 3 = \boxed{\phantom{0}}$

$7 \times 3 = \boxed{\phantom{0}}$   $2 \times 3 = \boxed{\phantom{0}}$   $6 \times 3 = \boxed{\phantom{0}}$

$10 \times 3 = \boxed{\phantom{0}}$   $4 \times 3 = \boxed{\phantom{0}}$   $8 \times 3 = \boxed{\phantom{0}}$

# Sharing among 3

Share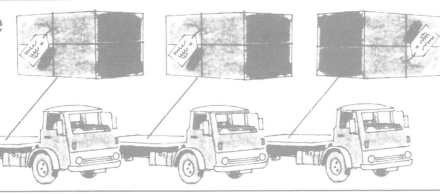

$\boxed{1}$ each

$3 \div 3 = \boxed{1}$

Share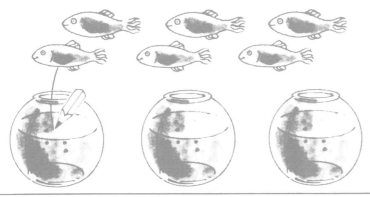

$\boxed{\phantom{0}}$ each

$6 \div 3 = \boxed{\phantom{0}}$

Share

$\boxed{\phantom{0}}$ each

$9 \div 3 = \boxed{\phantom{0}}$

Share

$\boxed{\phantom{0}}$ each

$12 \div 3 = \boxed{\phantom{0}}$

Share

$\boxed{\phantom{0}}$ each

$15 \div 3 = \boxed{\phantom{0}}$

27

# Sharing among 3

Share

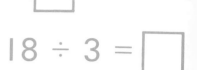 each

$18 \div 3 = \square$

Share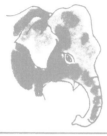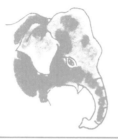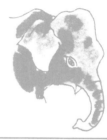

 each

$21 \div 3 = \square$

Share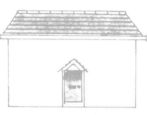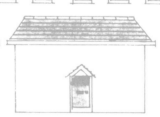

 each

$24 \div 3 = \square$

Share

 each

$27 \div 3 = \square$

Share

 each

$30 \div 3 = \square$

# 3s

$3 \div 3 = \boxed{1}$     $6 \div 3 = \boxed{\phantom{0}}$     $9 \div 3 = \boxed{\phantom{0}}$

$12 \div 3 = \boxed{\phantom{0}}$     $15 \div 3 = \boxed{\phantom{0}}$     $18 \div 3 = \boxed{\phantom{0}}$

$21 \div 3 = \boxed{\phantom{0}}$     $24 \div 3 = \boxed{\phantom{0}}$     $\div 3 = \boxed{\phantom{0}}$

                      $30 \div 3 = \boxed{\phantom{0}}$

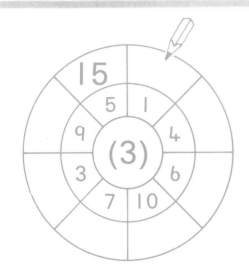 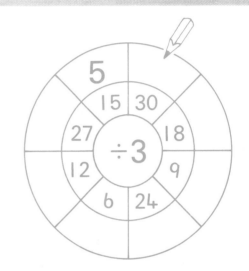

$1 \times 3 = \boxed{\phantom{0}}$     $6 \div 3 = \boxed{\phantom{0}}$     $9 \times 3 = \boxed{\phantom{0}}$

$18 \div 3 = \boxed{\phantom{0}}$     $27 \div 3 = \boxed{\phantom{0}}$     $3 \times 3 = \boxed{\phantom{0}}$

$24 \div 3 = \boxed{\phantom{0}}$     $5 \times 3 = \boxed{\phantom{0}}$     $12 \div 3 = \boxed{\phantom{0}}$

$15 \div 3 = \boxed{\phantom{0}}$     $2 \times 3 = \boxed{\phantom{0}}$     $4 \times 3 = \boxed{\phantom{0}}$

$7 \times 3 = \boxed{\phantom{0}}$     $30 \div 3 = \boxed{\phantom{0}}$     $3 \div 3 = \boxed{\phantom{0}}$

$6 \times 3 = \boxed{\phantom{0}}$     $9 \div 3 = \boxed{\phantom{0}}$     $10 \times 3 = \boxed{\phantom{0}}$

$21 \div 3 = \boxed{\phantom{0}}$                              $8 \times 3 = \boxed{\phantom{0}}$

# Picture problems

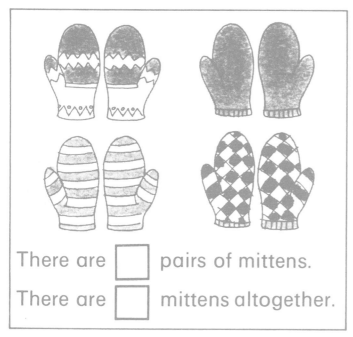

There are ☐ pairs of mittens.

There are ☐ mittens altogether.

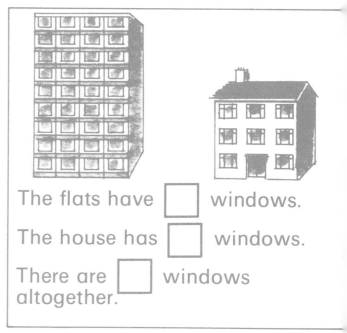

The flats have ☐ windows.

The house has ☐ windows.

There are ☐ windows altogether.

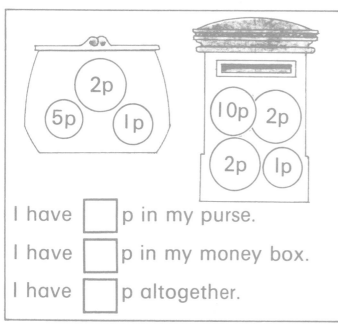

I have ☐ p in my purse.

I have ☐ p in my money box.

I have ☐ p altogether.

☐ has ☐ p.

☐ has ☐ p.

They have ☐ p altogether.

I had ☐ p.

I bought a teddy for ☐ p.

I have ☐ p change.

There are ☐ balloons altogether.

They have ☐ balloons each.